SPHERE

First published in Great Britain in 2015 by Sphere

3 5 7 9 10 8 6 4 2

The moral right of the author has been asserted.

A CIP catalogue record for this book
is available from the British Library.

ISBN 978-0-7515-6397-9

Printed in Italy

Sphere
An imprint of
Little, Brown Book Group
Carmelite House
50 Victoria Embankment
London EC4Y 0DZ

An Hachette UK Company
www.hachette.co.uk

www.littlebrown.co.uk

The Candy Crush Colouring Book

Creatively Colour the Candy Kingdom

sphere

Set in the magical world of the Candy Kingdom, it is here where we are introduced to its inhabitants Tiffi and Mr. Toffee, who owns the Candy Store in Candy Town.

Magic!

The delicious Candy Kingdom features divine landscapes, sweet patterns and the delectable super-sweet Candies.

All you need are pens, pencils and a bit of imagination to bring the magical world of Candy Crush Saga to life!

Sweet!

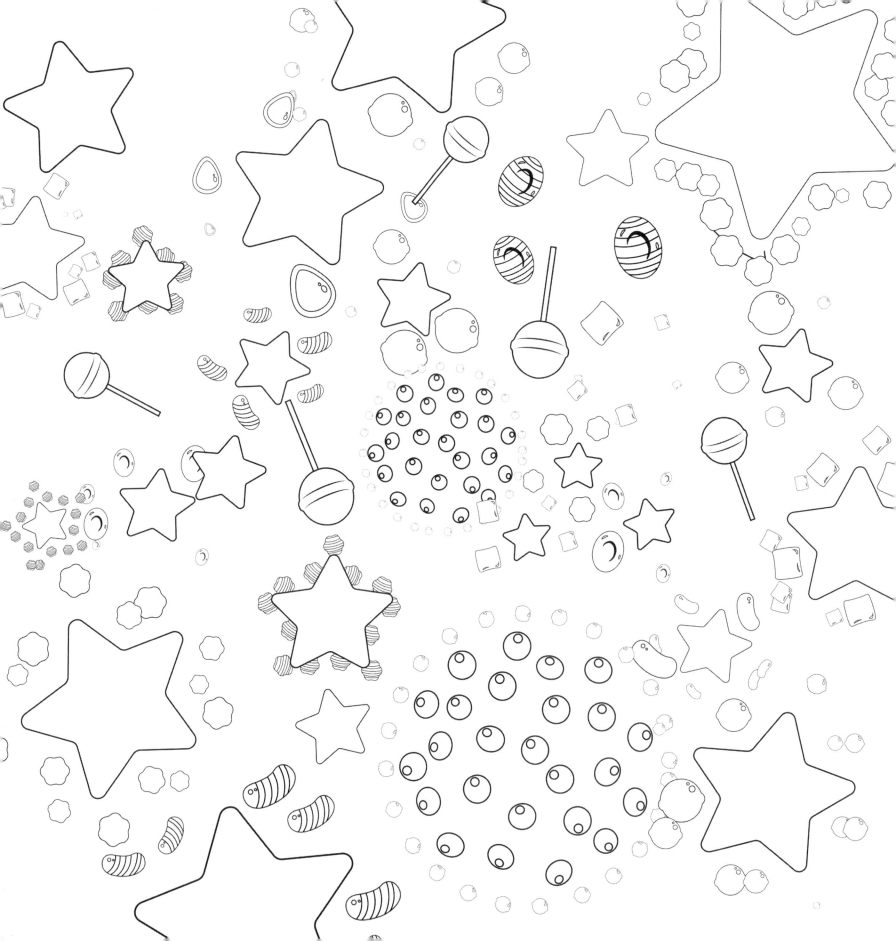

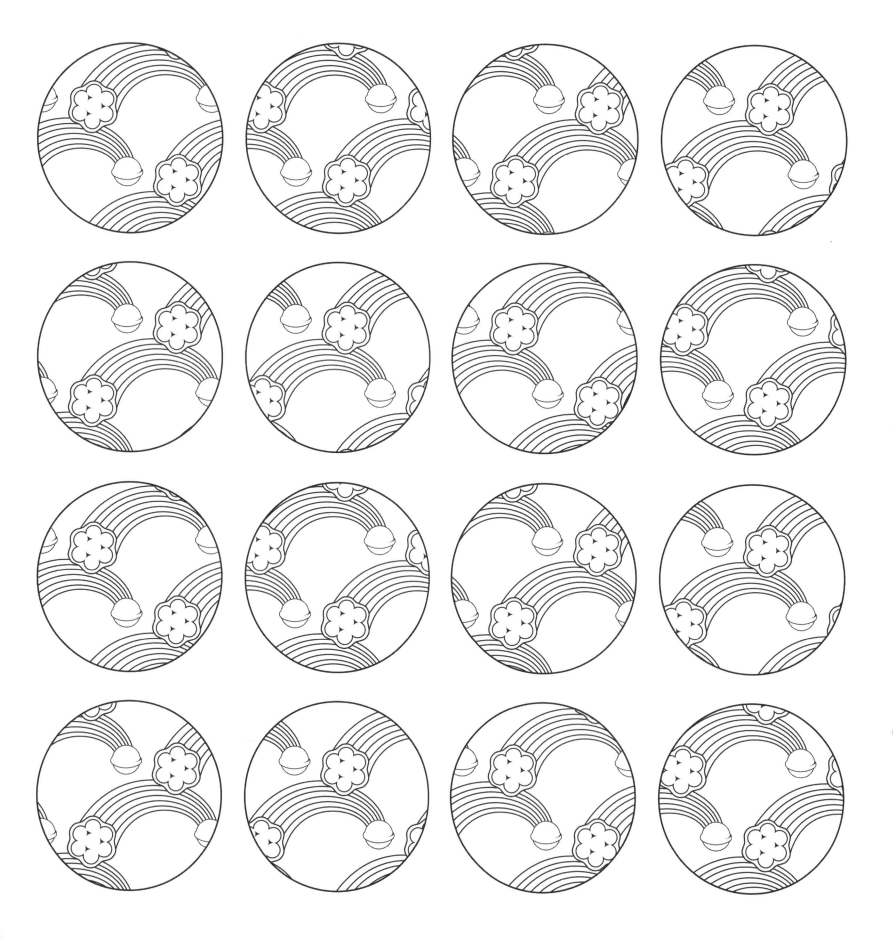

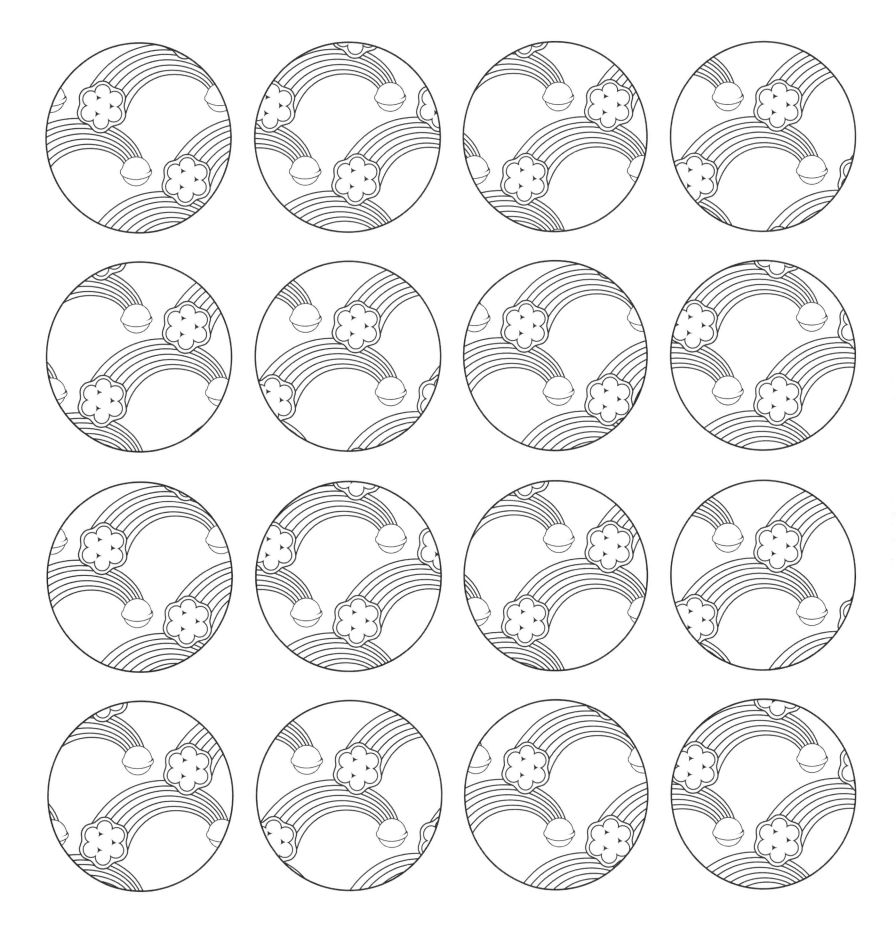

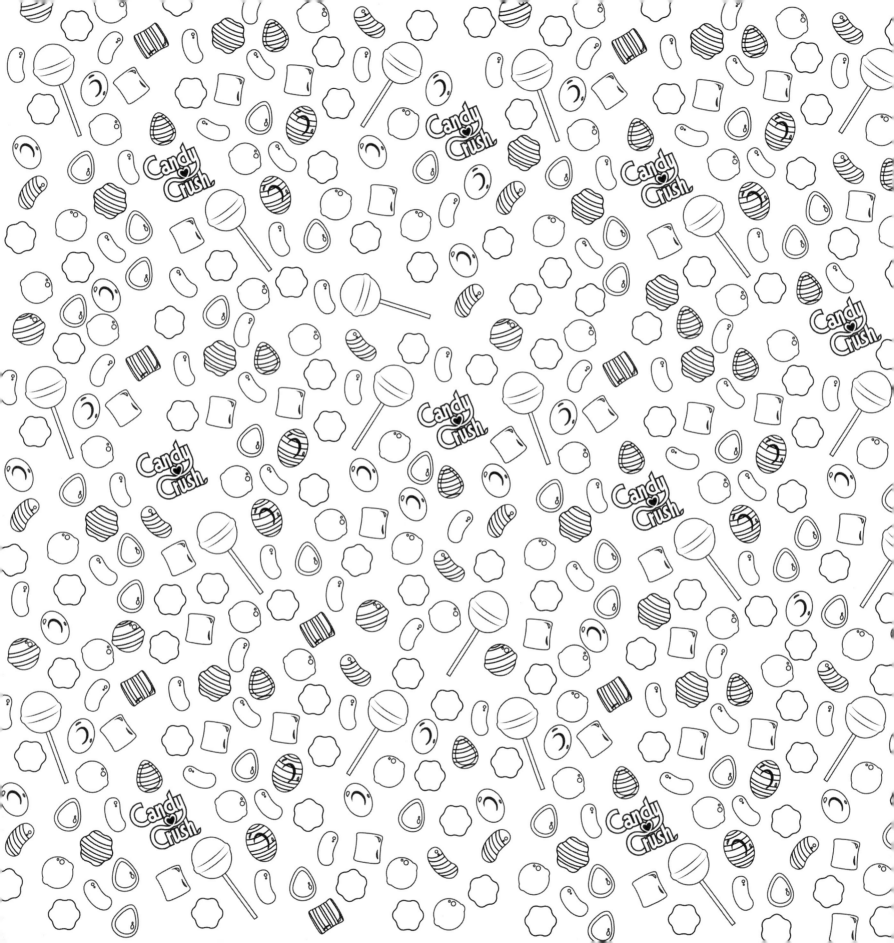

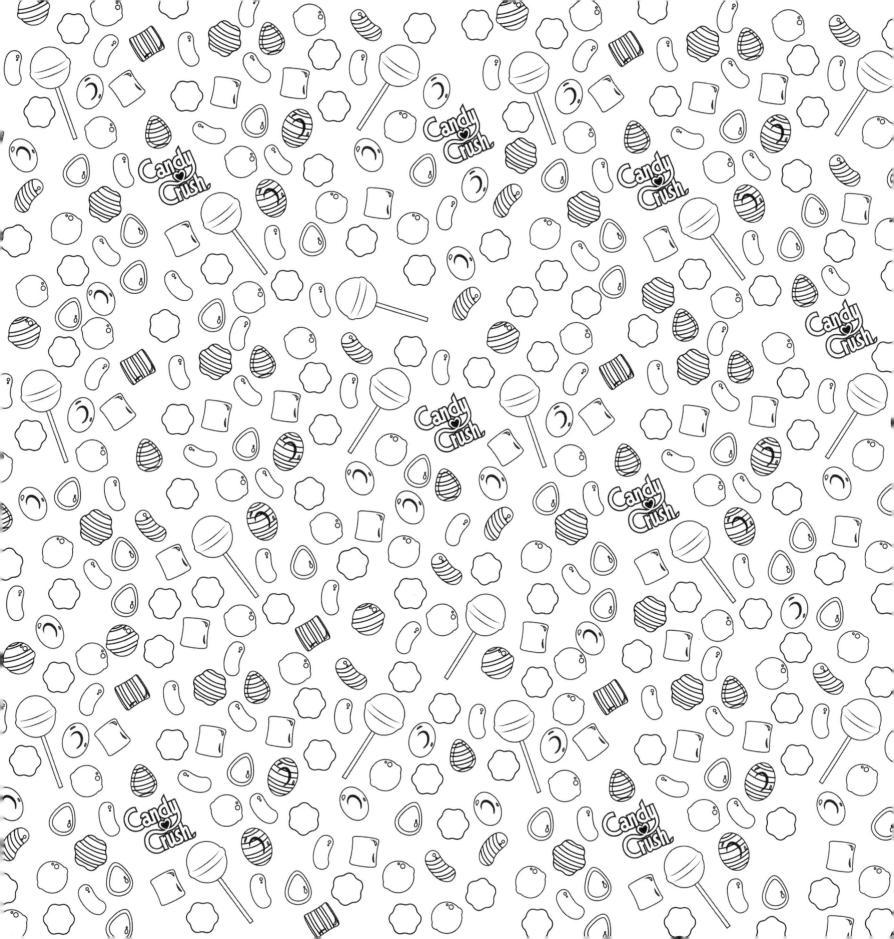

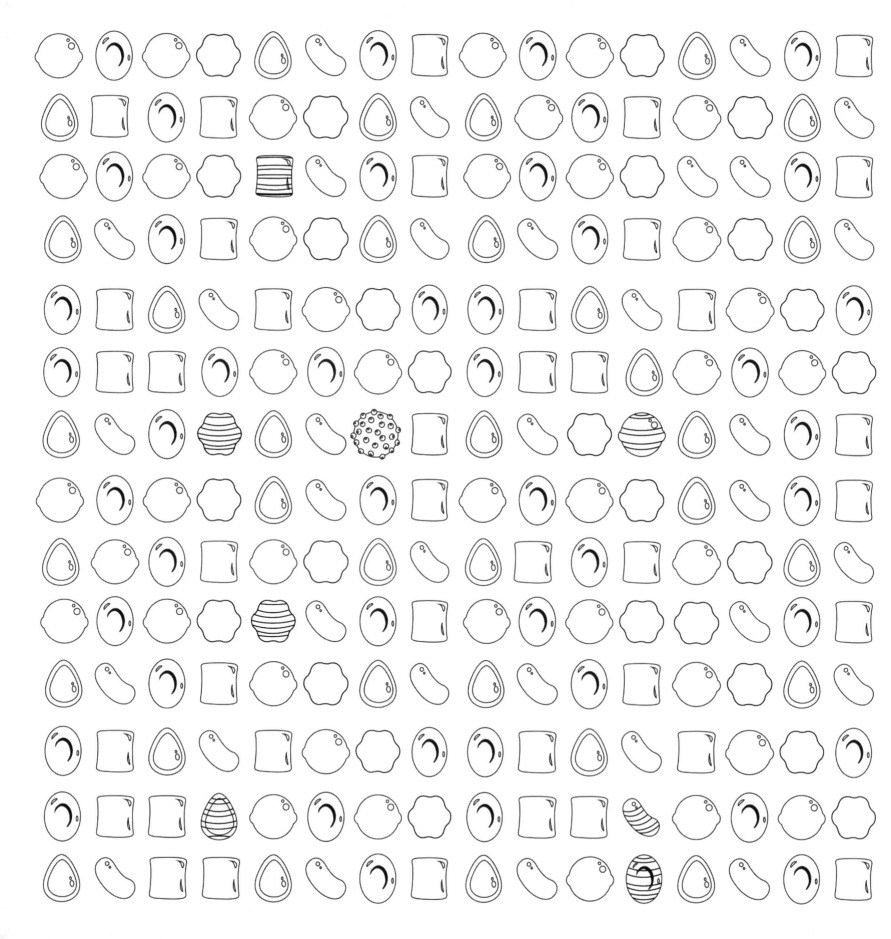

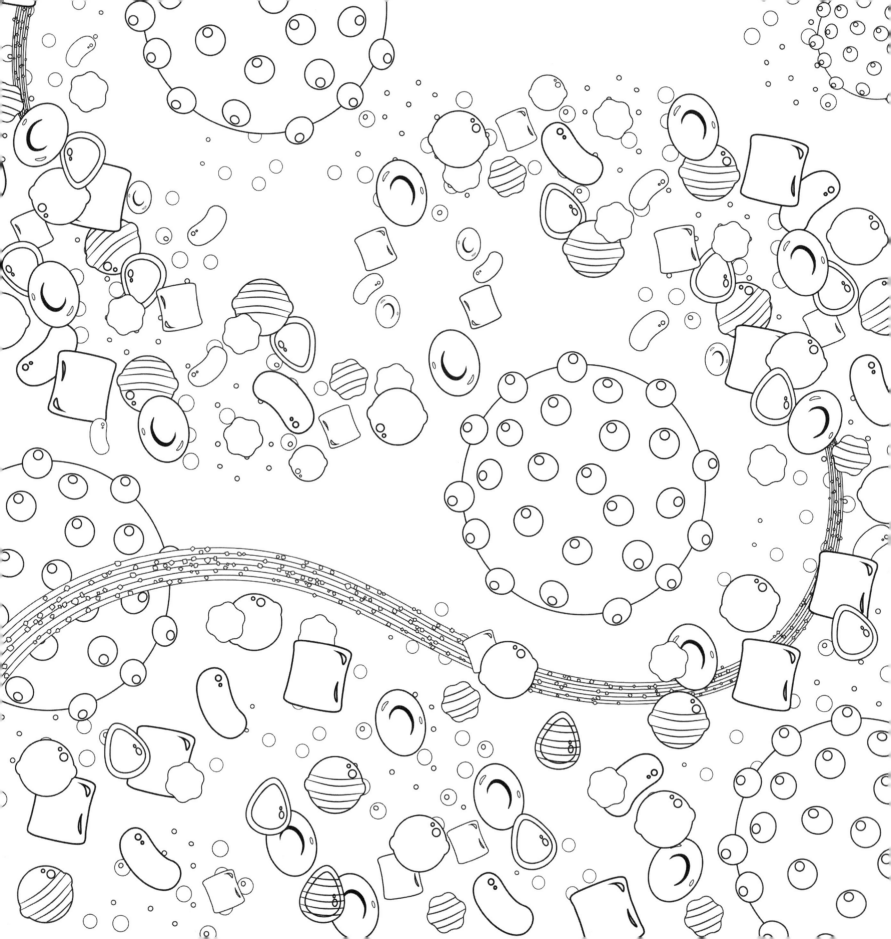

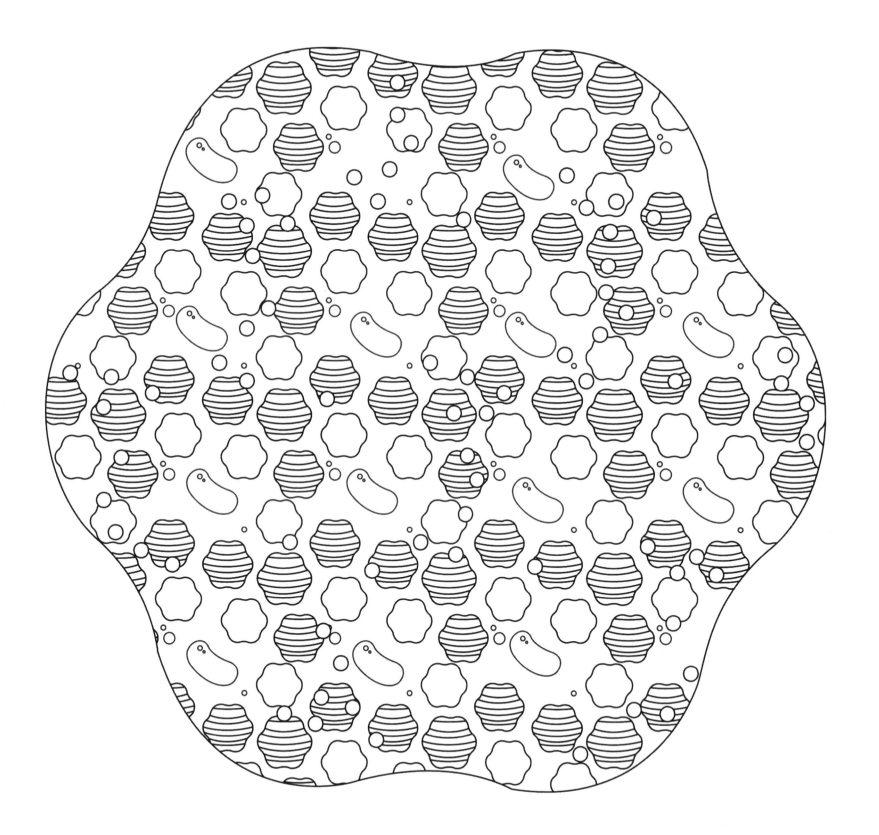

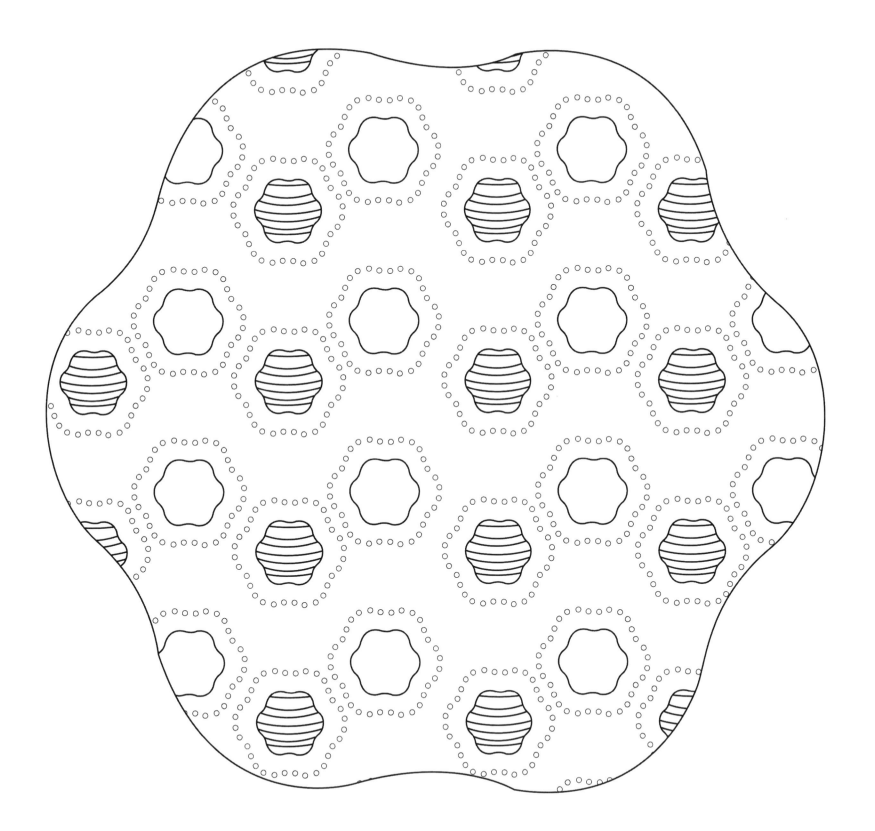

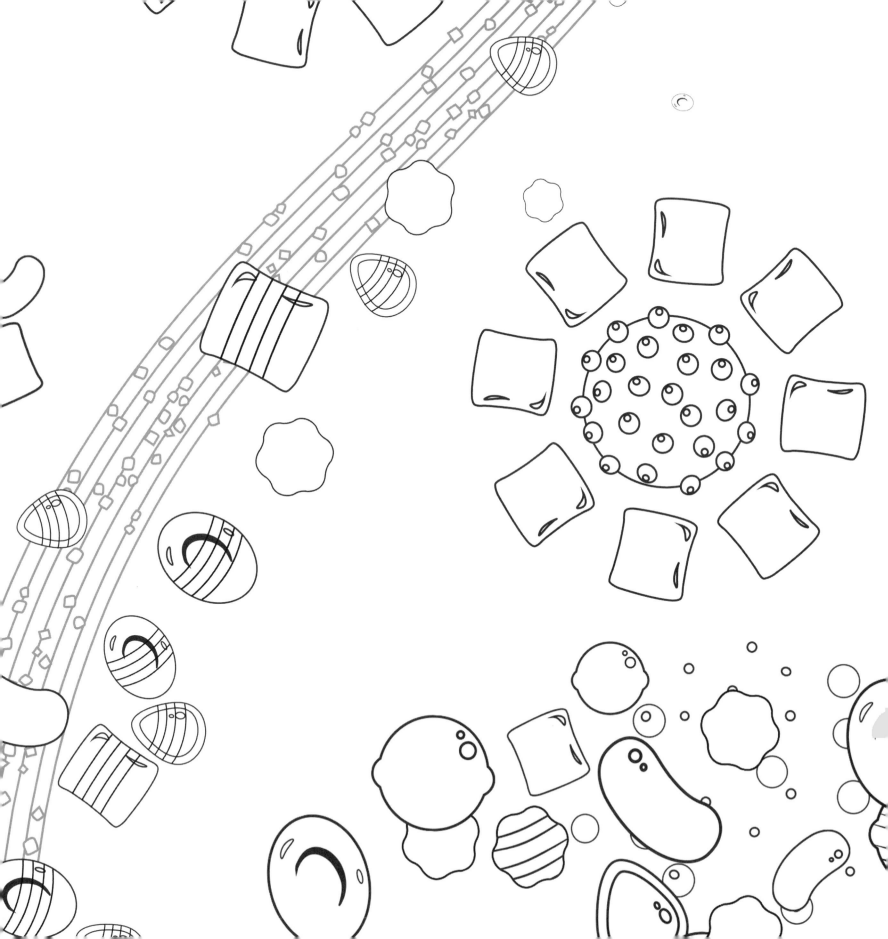

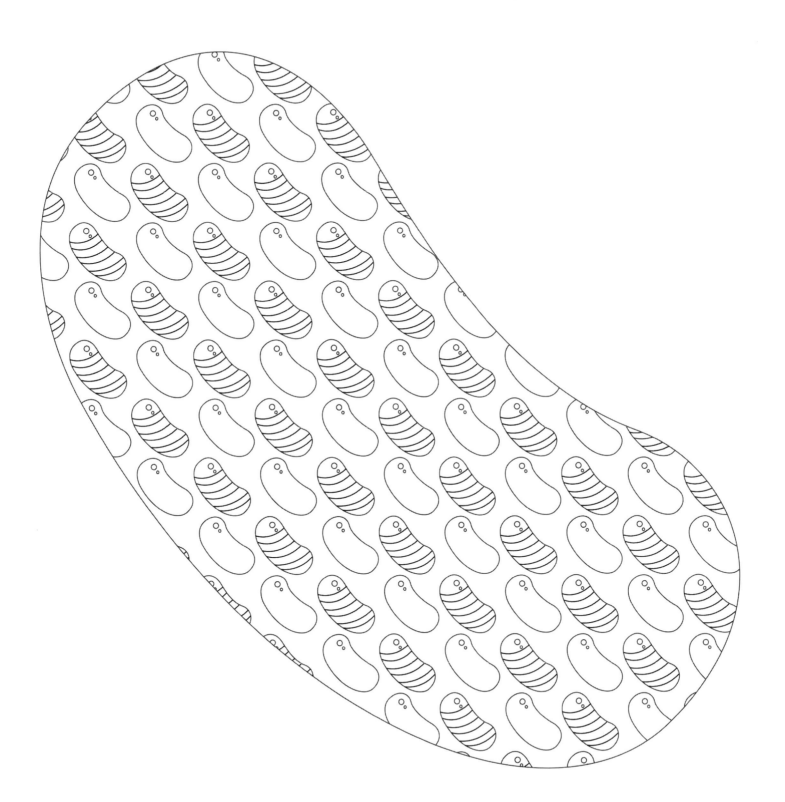

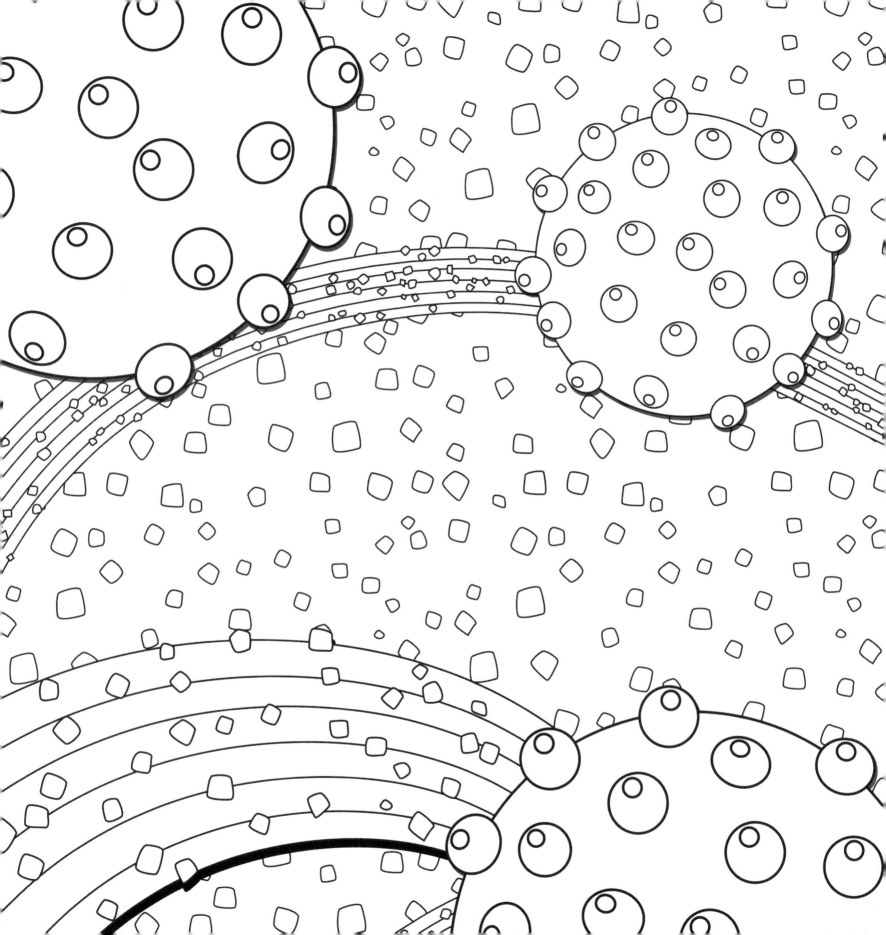

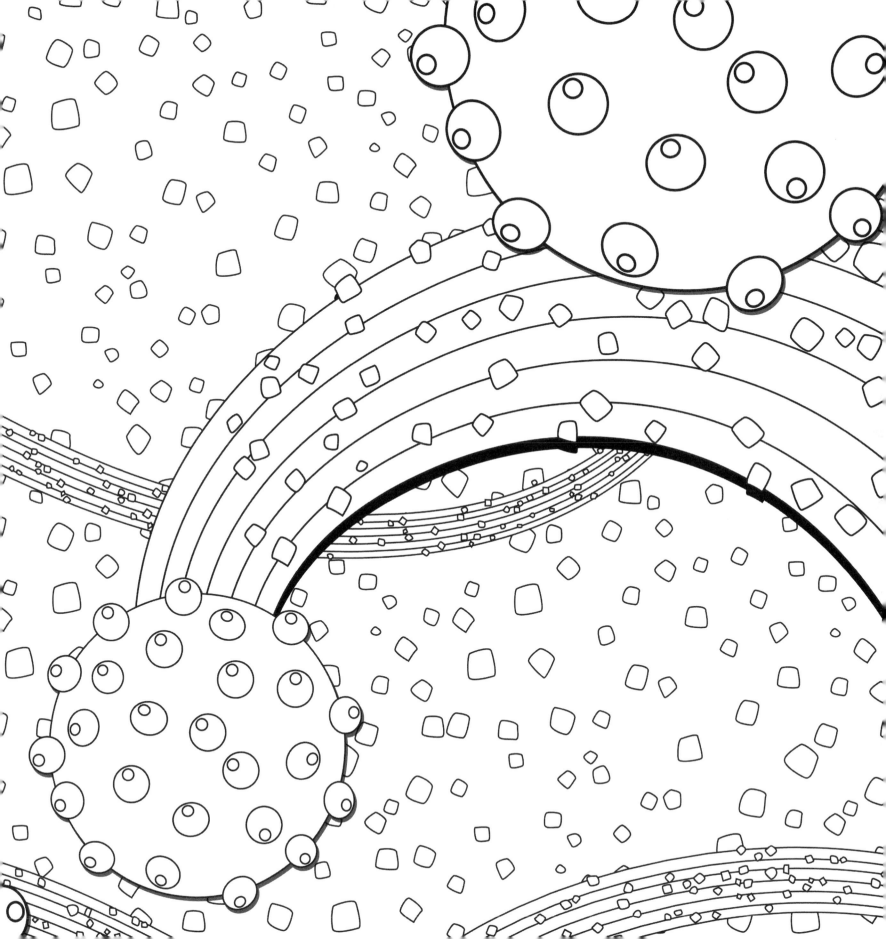

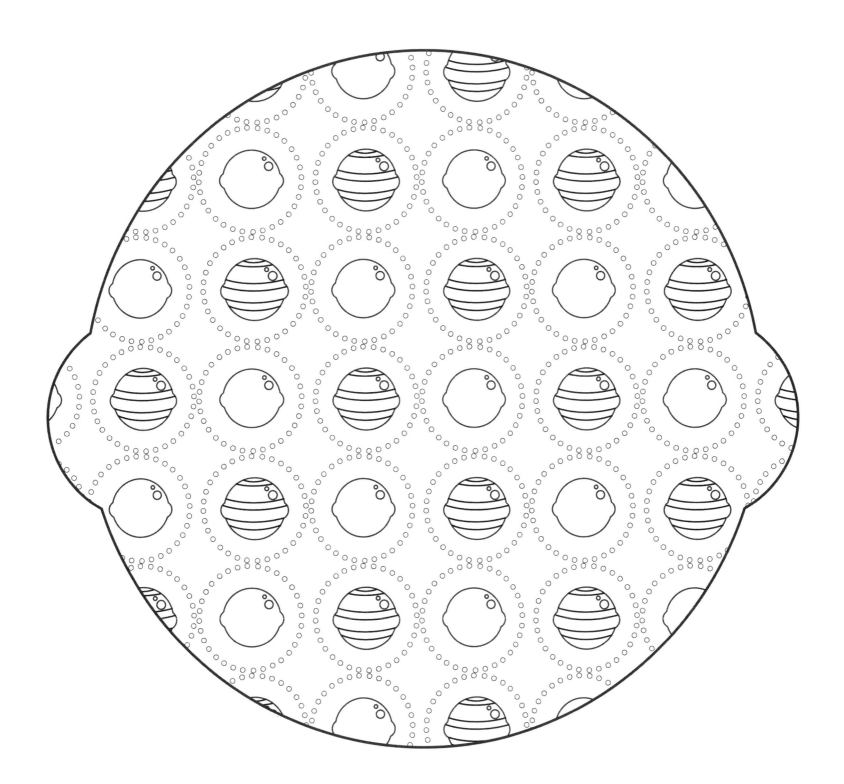

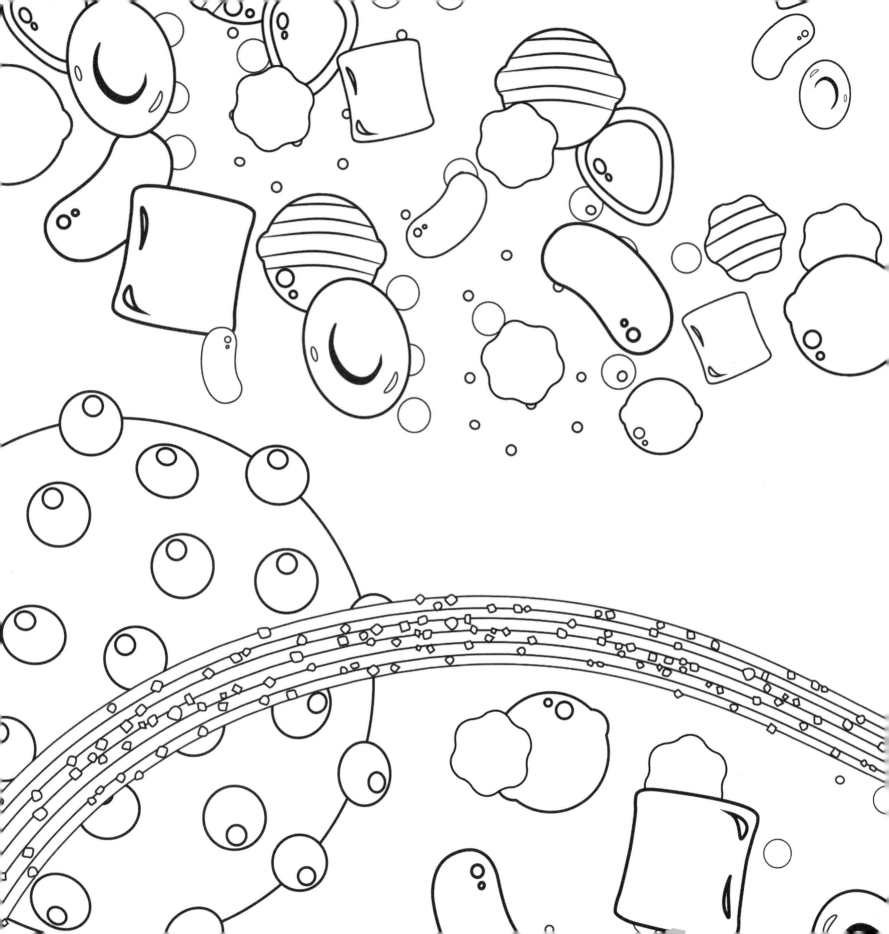

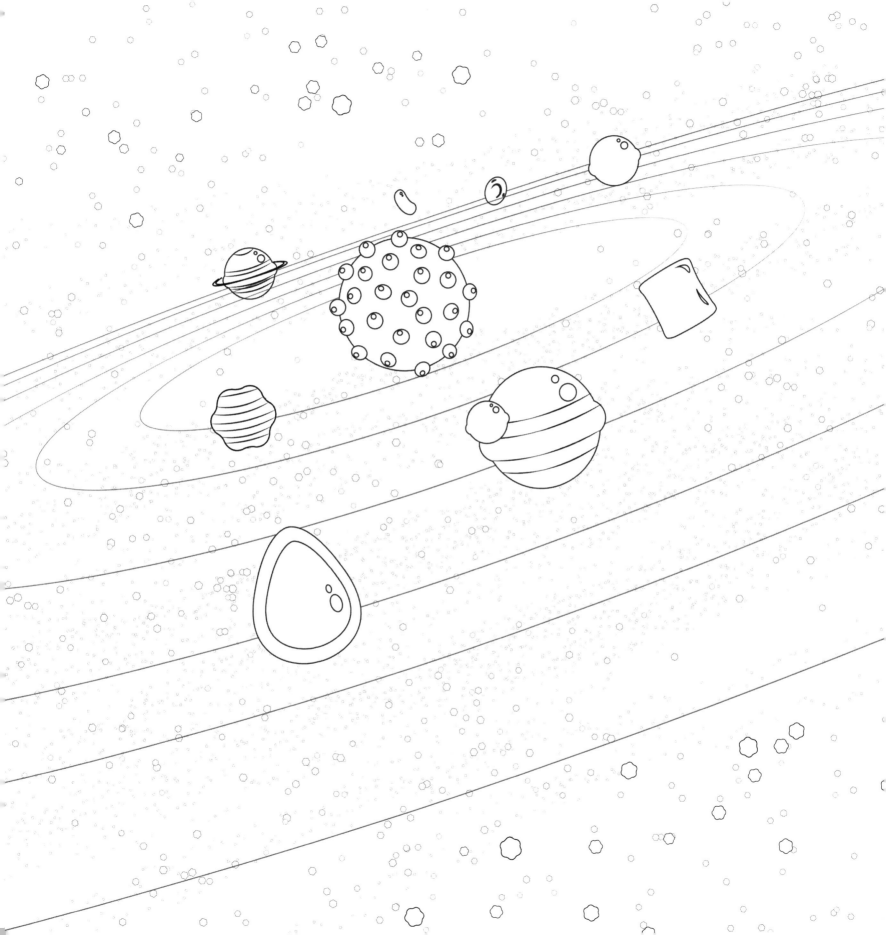

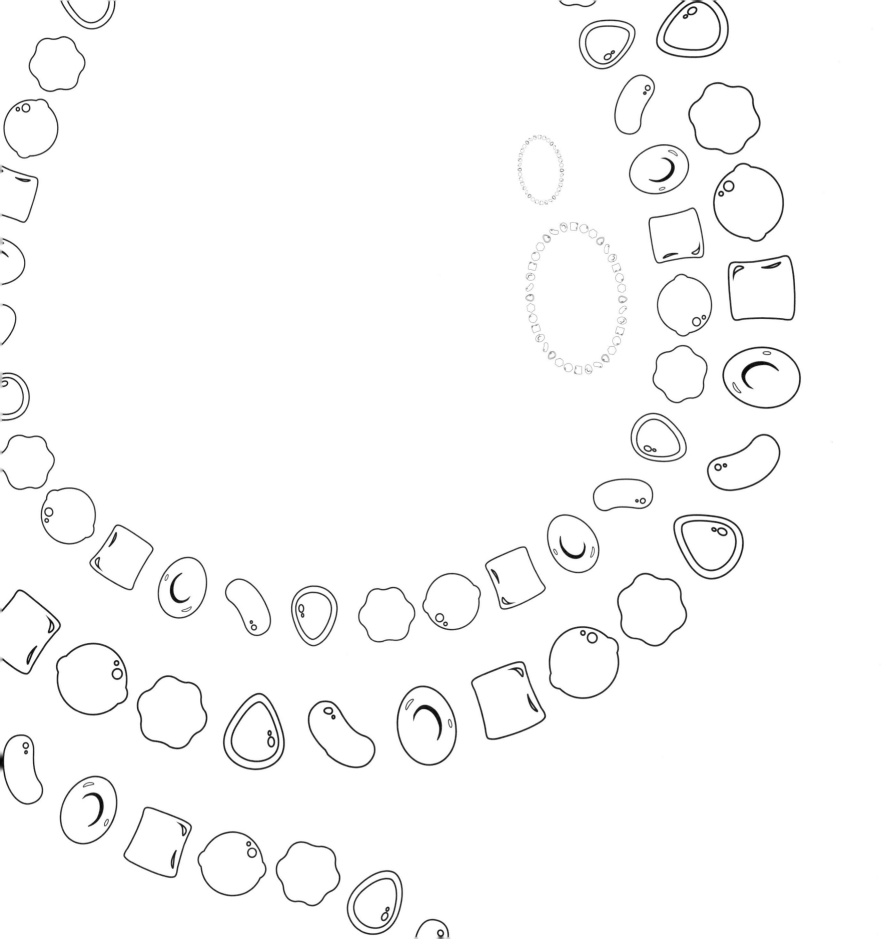

Make up your own
Candylicious designs!

Freestyle!

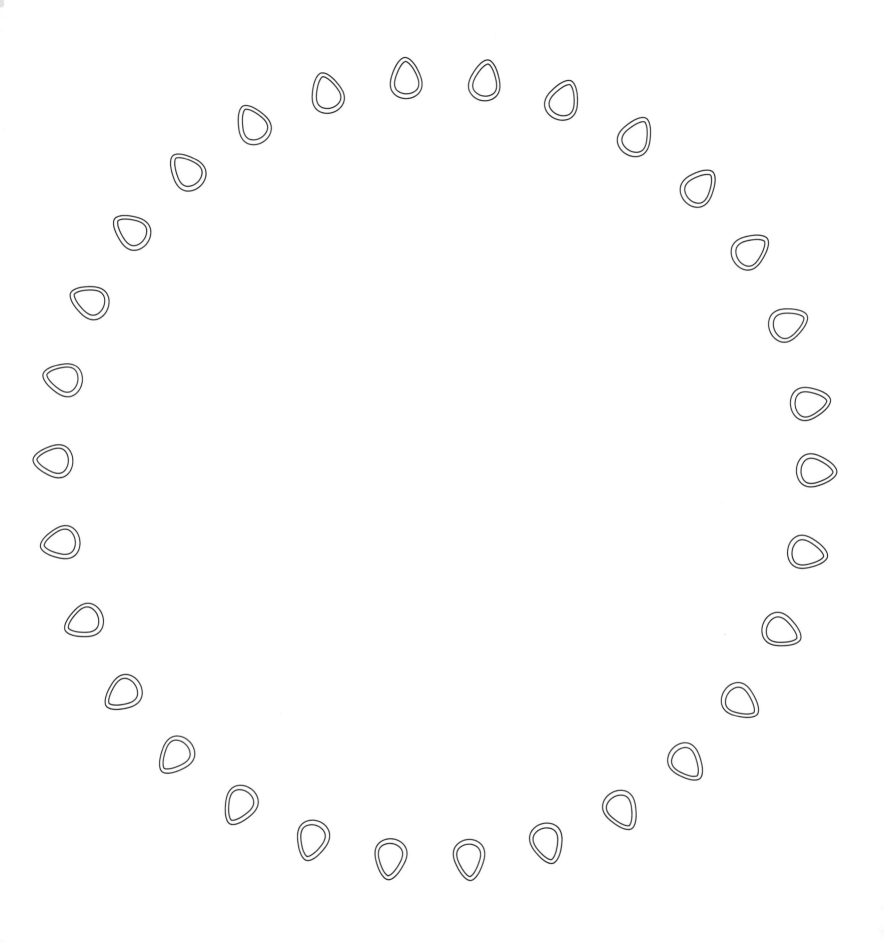

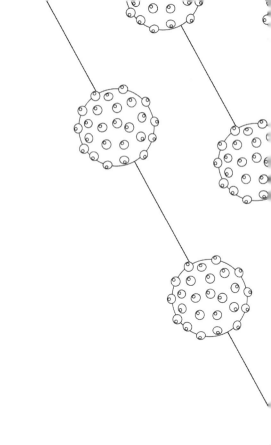

Delicious!

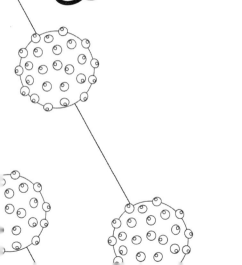

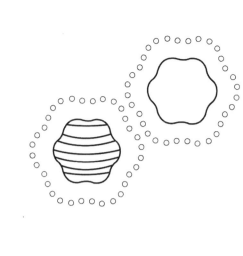

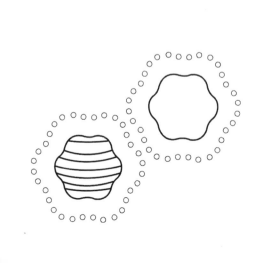

Crush! Delicious! Tasty! Sugar Crush! Delicious! Tasty! Sugar Crush! Delicious! Tasty! Sugar Crush! Delicious! Tasty! Sugar Crush! Delicious! Tasty! Sugar

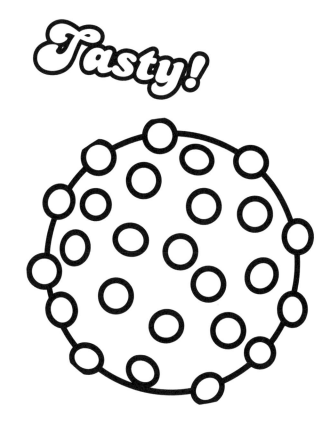